The Adventures of The Swamp Kids

The Missing Chord

Written by
Leif Nedland Pedersen

Layout and Illustrations by
Tim Banfell

Ally-Gator BookBites Publishing House

LAKE CHARLES, LA

Published by
Ally-Gator BookBites Publishing House
1428 Watkins Street
Lake Charles, LA 70601
www.allygatorbookbites.com

Printed in the U.S.A. through Bolton Associates, Inc.
San Rafael, CA 94901
www.boltonprinting.com

First Printing
ISBN# 978-0-9886332-2-3

Our books are yummy!

Look for other titles and merchandise at
www.theswampkids.com

This book is dedicated to the "kids"
who have helped us stay in our youth
much longer than we would have dreamed:

Dane Pedersen
and
Tim Banfell, Jr.

and to the ladies who have allowed us to
maintain that youthful outlook:

Sheryl Pedersen
and
Laurie Ann

A special thanks to Cajun music legend,
Doug Kershaw
for contributing our Lagniappe Lesson

and last, to our publisher,
who re-discovered us after fifteen years in hiding:

Tommie Townsley

There once was a swamp down in south Looziana,

a couple of miles from Mamou;

And in it a bayou, well hidden from daylight,

that everyone called Bayou Bleu.

The fireflies would light up the treetops at twilight,

their glow cast a Disney-like sheen;

And just around midnight the creatures would gather,

to sing and to dance and to dream.

Pierre a le Gator was raised on the bayou

and known for his way with a tune:

With Tutu the turtle and Campeaux the catfish

and Mon Cher the pretty raccoon.

The banks of the bayou had cypress as borders

with lily pads bunched in the middle;

And under the moonlight the friends would make music

that featured Pierre on the fiddle.

The washboard would ring like a chorus of cymbals,

as Tutu would strum with a dash;

And Mon Cher would dance with her red concertina

as Campeaux kept time with his splash.

A diddle ay iddle ayeeeeee,

a diddle ay iddle ayeeeeee;

The Swamp Kids would play until night turned to day,

a diddle ay iddle ayeeeeee!!!

They practiced and practiced to enter the contest

for number one band in the land;

But something was missing and though they kept listening,

the sound they came up with was bland.

Well, one little creature would watch from the distance

whenever the foursome would play;

"But what can I do," wondered Sashay the crawfish,

"to spice up their music some way?"

He crawled out the bayou and headed for daylight,

away from his friends and his home;

In order to help, he would roam the land over

to find just the right missing tone.

He searched through the village, then under a trestle

and plunked on each tin can and stick;

And finally he spotted a bright tub of metal

right next to some twine on a brick.

Soon back on the bayou, the fiddle was starting,

with Mon Cher and Tutu in place;

When out of the darkness, there came something magic,

the sound of a washing tub bass.

Said Tutu, "It's thrilling! The tone is amazing!"

Their sound filled the bayou with glee;

They played and they danced as they sang out their song,

a diddle ay iddle ayeeeeee!!!

A diddle ay iddle ayeeeeee,
a diddle ay iddle ayeeeeee;

They played and they danced as
they sang out their song,

A diddle ay iddle ayeeeeee!!!

The contest was held at the Fall Fais Do-Do,

with the Swamp Kids the very last band;

The crowd screamed for more with a thunderous roar

and proclaimed them the best in the land.

So if you should find that your talents are needed

but not sure if you could fit in;

Don't sit around waiting for something to happen;

just waiting is no way to win.

By making the effort to meet every challenge

and being the best you can be,

You'll find you're admired for just showing courage,

a diddle ay iddle ayeeeeee!!!

Lagniappe Lesson

By Cajun music legend, Doug Kershaw

Bonjour Mon Petit Amis *(Hello my little friends)...*

I think there are two important lessons that can be learned from the story you just read; the first is that sometime you have to "step out of the shadows" to overcome shyness. Many of us hold back what we want to say or do because we don't want to make a mistake or we aren't sure if we will fit in. This story tells us to "do what you think is right and take the chance." Sashay did just that and found there were new friends ready to welcome him into their group.

The second lesson means a lot to me because it is my Joi d'Vie *(joy of life)* – music. Sashay shows us that music comes from many sources: sometimes you learn music from a fine music school, from practicing your guitar chords in your living room or, as he has done, by making musical sounds from everyday materials. The important thing is the music itself. Without it, the world would be a very sad place. So, if music is something you are interested in, try all sorts of instruments until you find the one you like. Who knows...you may become a great country fiddler one day!

A diddle ay iddle ayeeeeee!!!

Doug Kershaw

Doug Kershaw is an award winning Cajun fiddler and singer who grew up in Cameron, LA, speaking only French until he was eight years old. He taught himself to play many instruments and made his mark on music as a Cajun fiddler recording numerous hits, including, "Diggy Liggy Lo" and "Louisiana Man." He holds a degree in Mathematics from McNeese State University and maintains a busy performance schedule throughout the U.S. and abroad.

Bringing the Swamp Kids to Life...

Being from the deep South certainly helped stimulate the creative juices of the writer and illustrator. Given the fact that both have been immersed in art, music and the rhythms that come from the streets of New Orleans on a daily basis, it was only natural that from those roots music would pour out in the form of poetic story-telling.

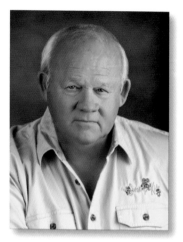

Leif N. Pedersen hails from New Orleans and lives in Slidell, Louisiana. He has been a singer for almost 40 years and spent a half dozen of those years as the featured vocalist with Buddy Morrow's Tommy Dorsey Orchestra. It is from those years that the rhyming style of the "Adventures" evolved. Leif is a former Marine and a member of Southeastern Louisiana University's Music Hall of Fame. For the past 25 years, he has worked as a professional fundraising executive and leader of the 14-piece, 1944 Big Band. *"While my Norwegian "Pedersen-side" certainly has dominated most of my lifelong persona, it is my mother's "Fourrier" side and long lineage of Cajun connections back to Louis XVI that have stimulated my love for Cajun lore. I have tried to bring this to life in these adventures."*

Tim Banfell also resides in Slidell, Louisiana and is an accomplished cartoonist and graphic designer. He has a way of using his unique artistic ability in making his characters magically come to life on paper. He has developed a devoted following for his self-syndicated comic strip, *Wrong Key*, which is featured in numerous newspapers around the coast of Florida. While his profession as a graphic designer and photographer for Shell Projects & Technology keeps him in the New Orleans area, weekend road trips back to his hometown of Pensacola, Florida provide constant fuel for his comic strip about beachcombers and fishermen wading through the high and low tides of life. Visit his website at www.wrongkeycomicstrip.com.

Make Your Own Wash Tub Bass

Hey Kids, here's a project you and Dad or Mom can do at home to make your own, playable Wash Tub Bass just like **The Swamp Kids** play.

You'll Need:

- *A Ball of Twine*
- *4 ft. Stick (Dowel)*
- *Small Galvanized Wash Tub*
- *Tools: Drill, File & Scissors*

Assembly:

1. Drill a hole 1" down in the center of one end of the stick, big enough to fit the twine through. On the other end, file a ½" deep groove in the middle.

2. Next, drill a hole in the center of the bottom of the wash tub, just big enough for the twine to fit through.

3. With the wash tub facing upside down, push the twine through the hole and tie it off in knots underneath so it can't come out when pulled.

4. Place the groove end of the stick on the rim of the tub and hold it up straight over the center hole in the wash tub.

5. Pull the twine through the drilled hole at the top of the stick and tie it off on the other side with a couple of knots until it's tight, then cut the remainder off.

Now, you're ready to play your own Wash Tub Bass!

How to play:

Place your foot on the rim of the wash tub to hold it down while holding the stick in one hand at the top.

"Plunk" the twine with your other hand (fingers) while moving your stick hand away from the center position to make the notes sound higher and straight up to the center for a lower pitch.

Enjoy!

Join the Adventure!

www.theswampkids.com